June Vacation

by Rachel Fogelberg

HOUGHTON MIFFLIN

BOSTON

PHOTOGRAPHY CREDITS: Cover © David Braun/Masterfile; Toc © Red Images, LLC/Alamy; 2 © Susan Van Etten/ PhotoEdit; 3 © Blend Images; 4 © David Braun/Masterfile; 5 © Red Images, LLC/Alamy; 6 © Lars Klove Photo Service/ Riser/Getty Images; 7 © Steve Skjold/Alamy; 8 © Jeff Greenberg/PhotoEdit; 9 © CORBIS; 10 © imagebroker/Alamy

Printed in China

ISBN-13: 978-0-547-01711-2
ISBN-10: 0-547-01711-1

12 13 14 15 0940 17 16 15 14
4500496268

I am out of school now.

I can go to the park.
I like to play ball
in the park.

I can have a picnic.
I like to sit
on the grass.

I like to walk
in the woods.

I like to read.
I can read
on the porch.

I can paint a picture.
I like to paint.

I like to fish.
I can catch a fish.

I can go to the pool.
I like to swim.

I can swing.
And you can swing
with me!

Responding

✔ **TARGET SKILL** **Compare and Contrast** How is being in school different from being on summer vacation? How is it the same?

Write About It

Text to World Draw a picture of some children having fun on their summer vacation. Write a sentence about your picture.